starters and snacks

Recipe --

Serves _____ Preparation time _____

Difficulty Scale [1 | 2 | 3 | 4 | 5] Cooking time _____

Ingredients

Name   Weight/Measure/Amount

------------------------------------   ------------------------------------

------------------------------------   ------------------------------------

------------------------------------   ------------------------------------

------------------------------------   ------------------------------------

------------------------------------   ------------------------------------

------------------------------------   ------------------------------------

------------------------------------   ------------------------------------

Method

Recipe

Serves _____ Preparation time _____

Difficulty Scale [1][2][3][4][5] Cooking time _____

Ingredients

Name	Weight/Measure/Amount

Method

Recipe ---

Serves _____   Preparation time _____

Difficulty Scale | 1 | 2 | 3 | 4 | 5 | Cooking time   _____

Ingredients

Name   Weight/Measure/Amount

-------------------------------   -------------------------------

-------------------------------   -------------------------------

-------------------------------   -------------------------------

-------------------------------   -------------------------------

-------------------------------   -------------------------------

-------------------------------   -------------------------------

-------------------------------   -------------------------------

Method

Recipe

Serves _____   Preparation time _____

Difficulty Scale | 1 | 2 | 3 | 4 | 5 | Cooking time _____

Ingredients

Name	Weight/Measure/Amount
--------------------------	--------------------------
--------------------------	--------------------------
--------------------------	--------------------------
--------------------------	--------------------------
--------------------------	--------------------------
--------------------------	--------------------------
--------------------------	--------------------------

Method

Recipe

Serves _____   Preparation time _____

Difficulty Scale   1 2 3 4 5   Cooking time _____

Ingredients

Name   Weight/Measure/Amount

----------------------------   ----------------------------
----------------------------   ----------------------------
----------------------------   ----------------------------
----------------------------   ----------------------------
----------------------------   ----------------------------
----------------------------   ----------------------------
----------------------------   ----------------------------

Method

Recipe

Serves _____ Preparation time _____

Difficulty Scale [1] [2] [3] [4] [5] Cooking time _____

Ingredients

Name   Weight/Measure/Amount

---------------------------------------   ---------------------------------------

---------------------------------------   ---------------------------------------

---------------------------------------   ---------------------------------------

---------------------------------------   ---------------------------------------

---------------------------------------   ---------------------------------------

---------------------------------------   ---------------------------------------

---------------------------------------   ---------------------------------------

Method

Recipe --

Serves _____   Preparation time _____

Difficulty Scale | 1 | 2 | 3 | 4 | 5 | Cooking time   _____

Ingredients

Name   Weight/Measure/Amount

------------------------------   ------------------------------

------------------------------   ------------------------------

------------------------------   ------------------------------

------------------------------   ------------------------------

------------------------------   ------------------------------

------------------------------   ------------------------------

------------------------------   ------------------------------

Method

Recipe --

Serves _____ Preparation time _____

Difficulty Scale | 1 | 2 | 3 | 4 | 5 | Cooking time _____

Ingredients

Name   Weight/Measure/Amount

------------------------------   ------------------------------

------------------------------   ------------------------------

------------------------------   ------------------------------

------------------------------   ------------------------------

------------------------------   ------------------------------

------------------------------   ------------------------------

------------------------------   ------------------------------

Method

Recipe ....

Serves _____   Preparation time _____

Difficulty Scale   1 2 3 4 5   Cooking time _____

Ingredients

Name   Weight/Measure/Amount

-----------------------------   -----------------------------

-----------------------------   -----------------------------

-----------------------------   -----------------------------

-----------------------------   -----------------------------

-----------------------------   -----------------------------

-----------------------------   -----------------------------

-----------------------------   -----------------------------

Method

Recipe

Serves _____ Preparation time _____

Difficulty Scale [1 | 2 | 3 | 4 | 5] Cooking time _____

Ingredients

Name   Weight/Measure/Amount

------------------------------------   ------------------------------------

------------------------------------   ------------------------------------

------------------------------------   ------------------------------------

------------------------------------   ------------------------------------

------------------------------------   ------------------------------------

------------------------------------   ------------------------------------

------------------------------------   ------------------------------------

Method

----

place recipes here

place recipes here

salads, stir-fries and pasta

Recipe

Serves _____ Preparation time _____

Difficulty Scale | 1 | 2 | 3 | 4 | 5 | Cooking time _____

Ingredients

Name	Weight/Measure/Amount

Method

Recipe

Serves _____ Preparation time _____

Difficulty Scale [1] [2] [3] [4] [5]   Cooking time _____

Ingredients

Name	Weight/Measure/Amount

Method

Recipe ....

Serves _____ Preparation time _____

Difficulty Scale [1] [2] [3] [4] [5] Cooking time _____

Ingredients

Name   Weight/Measure/Amount

----------------------------------   ----------------------------------

----------------------------------   ----------------------------------

----------------------------------   ----------------------------------

----------------------------------   ----------------------------------

----------------------------------   ----------------------------------

----------------------------------   ----------------------------------

----------------------------------   ----------------------------------

Method

Recipe _____

Serves _____ Preparation time _____

Difficulty Scale [1 | 2 | 3 | 4 | 5] Cooking time _____

Ingredients

Name	Weight/Measure/Amount

Method

Recipe

Serves _____   Preparation time _____

Difficulty Scale [1] [2] [3] [4] [5]   Cooking time _____

Ingredients

Name   Weight/Measure/Amount

----------------------------------   ----------------------------------

----------------------------------   ----------------------------------

----------------------------------   ----------------------------------

----------------------------------   ----------------------------------

----------------------------------   ----------------------------------

----------------------------------   ----------------------------------

----------------------------------   ----------------------------------

Method

Recipe

_____

Serves _____   Preparation time _____

Difficulty Scale | 1 | 2 | 3 | 4 | 5 | Cooking time _____

Ingredients

Name   Weight/Measure/Amount

-------------------------------   -------------------------------

-------------------------------   -------------------------------

-------------------------------   -------------------------------

-------------------------------   -------------------------------

-------------------------------   -------------------------------

-------------------------------   -------------------------------

-------------------------------   -------------------------------

Method

Recipe ---

Serves _____   Preparation time _____

Difficulty Scale | 1 | 2 | 3 | 4 | 5 | Cooking time _____

Ingredients

Name	Weight/Measure/Amount
-------------------------------	-------------------------------
-------------------------------	-------------------------------
-------------------------------	-------------------------------
-------------------------------	-------------------------------
-------------------------------	-------------------------------
-------------------------------	-------------------------------
-------------------------------	-------------------------------

Method

Recipe --

Serves _____ Preparation time _____

Difficulty Scale [1] [2] [3] [4] [5]   Cooking time _____

Ingredients

Name   Weight/Measure/Amount

----------------------------------   ----------------------------------

----------------------------------   ----------------------------------

----------------------------------   ----------------------------------

----------------------------------   ----------------------------------

----------------------------------   ----------------------------------

----------------------------------   ----------------------------------

----------------------------------   ----------------------------------

Method

Recipe

....

Serves .... Preparation time ....

Difficulty Scale [1] [2] [3] [4] [5]   Cooking time ....

Ingredients

Name   Weight/Measure/Amount

-----------------------------------   -----------------------------------

-----------------------------------   -----------------------------------

-----------------------------------   -----------------------------------

-----------------------------------   -----------------------------------

-----------------------------------   -----------------------------------

-----------------------------------   -----------------------------------

-----------------------------------   -----------------------------------

Method

Recipe

Serves _____   Preparation time _____

Difficulty Scale | 1 | 2 | 3 | 4 | 5 | Cooking time _____

Ingredients

Name   Weight/Measure/Amount

-----------------------------------   -----------------------------------

-----------------------------------   -----------------------------------

-----------------------------------   -----------------------------------

-----------------------------------   -----------------------------------

-----------------------------------   -----------------------------------

-----------------------------------   -----------------------------------

-----------------------------------   -----------------------------------

Method

----

place recipes here

place recipes here

meat, fish and poultry

Recipe --

Serves _____ Preparation time _____

Difficulty Scale [1][2][3][4][5] Cooking time _____

Ingredients

Name	Weight/Measure/Amount
-----------------------------	-----------------------------
-----------------------------	-----------------------------
-----------------------------	-----------------------------
-----------------------------	-----------------------------
-----------------------------	-----------------------------
-----------------------------	-----------------------------
-----------------------------	-----------------------------

Method

Recipe

_____

Serves _____ Preparation time _____

Difficulty Scale | 1 | 2 | 3 | 4 | 5 | Cooking time _____

Ingredients

Name   Weight/Measure/Amount

------------------------------------   ------------------------------------

------------------------------------   ------------------------------------

------------------------------------   ------------------------------------

------------------------------------   ------------------------------------

------------------------------------   ------------------------------------

------------------------------------   ------------------------------------

------------------------------------   ------------------------------------

Method

Recipe --

Serves _____   Preparation time _____

Difficulty Scale | 1 | 2 | 3 | 4 | 5 | Cooking time _____

Ingredients

Name   Weight/Measure/Amount

----------------------------------   ----------------------------------

----------------------------------   ----------------------------------

----------------------------------   ----------------------------------

----------------------------------   ----------------------------------

----------------------------------   ----------------------------------

----------------------------------   ----------------------------------

----------------------------------   ----------------------------------

Method

Recipe

Serves _____ Preparation time _____

Difficulty Scale 1 2 3 4 5   Cooking time _____

Ingredients

Name	Weight/Measure/Amount

Method

Recipe

Serves _____   Preparation time _____

Difficulty Scale   [1] [2] [3] [4] [5]   Cooking time   _____

Ingredients

Name   Weight/Measure/Amount

-----------------------------------   -----------------------------------

-----------------------------------   -----------------------------------

-----------------------------------   -----------------------------------

-----------------------------------   -----------------------------------

-----------------------------------   -----------------------------------

-----------------------------------   -----------------------------------

-----------------------------------   -----------------------------------

Method

Recipe --

Serves _____ Preparation time _____

Difficulty Scale | 1 | 2 | 3 | 4 | 5 | Cooking time _____

Ingredients

Name	Weight/Measure/Amount
----------------------------	----------------------------
----------------------------	----------------------------
----------------------------	----------------------------
----------------------------	----------------------------
----------------------------	----------------------------
----------------------------	----------------------------
----------------------------	----------------------------

Method

Recipe

Serves _____ Preparation time _____

Difficulty Scale [1] [2] [3] [4] [5] Cooking time _____

Ingredients

Name   Weight/Measure/Amount

----------------------------- -----------------------------

----------------------------- -----------------------------

----------------------------- -----------------------------

----------------------------- -----------------------------

----------------------------- -----------------------------

----------------------------- -----------------------------

----------------------------- -----------------------------

Method

Recipe

Serves _____ Preparation time _____

Difficulty Scale [1 | 2 | 3 | 4 | 5] Cooking time _____

Ingredients

Name	Weight/Measure/Amount
------------------------------------	------------------------------------
------------------------------------	------------------------------------
------------------------------------	------------------------------------
------------------------------------	------------------------------------
------------------------------------	------------------------------------
------------------------------------	------------------------------------
------------------------------------	------------------------------------

Method

Recipe

_____

Serves _____ Preparation time _____

Difficulty Scale [1 | 2 | 3 | 4 | 5] Cooking time _____

Ingredients

Name	Weight/Measure/Amount
-----------------------------	-----------------------------
-----------------------------	-----------------------------
-----------------------------	-----------------------------
-----------------------------	-----------------------------
-----------------------------	-----------------------------
-----------------------------	-----------------------------
-----------------------------	-----------------------------

Method

Recipe

Serves _____   Preparation time _____

Difficulty Scale | 1 | 2 | 3 | 4 | 5 | Cooking time _____

Ingredients

Name	Weight/Measure/Amount
--------------------------------	--------------------------------
--------------------------------	--------------------------------
--------------------------------	--------------------------------
--------------------------------	--------------------------------
--------------------------------	--------------------------------
--------------------------------	--------------------------------
--------------------------------	--------------------------------

Method

Recipe _____

Serves _____ Preparation time _____

Difficulty Scale | 1 | 2 | 3 | 4 | 5 | Cooking time _____

Ingredients

Name   Weight/Measure/Amount

------------------------------------   ------------------------------------
------------------------------------   ------------------------------------
------------------------------------   ------------------------------------
------------------------------------   ------------------------------------
------------------------------------   ------------------------------------
------------------------------------   ------------------------------------
------------------------------------   ------------------------------------

Method

Recipe

Serves _____ Preparation time _____

Difficulty Scale [1][2][3][4][5] Cooking time _____

Ingredients

Name   Weight/Measure/Amount

------------------------------------   ------------------------------------

------------------------------------   ------------------------------------

------------------------------------   ------------------------------------

------------------------------------   ------------------------------------

------------------------------------   ------------------------------------

------------------------------------   ------------------------------------

------------------------------------   ------------------------------------

Method

Recipe

_____

Serves _____ Preparation time _____

Difficulty Scale | 1 | 2 | 3 | 4 | 5 | Cooking time _____

Ingredients

Name   Weight/Measure/Amount

-------------------------------------   -------------------------------------

-------------------------------------   -------------------------------------

-------------------------------------   -------------------------------------

-------------------------------------   -------------------------------------

-------------------------------------   -------------------------------------

-------------------------------------   -------------------------------------

-------------------------------------   -------------------------------------

Method

Recipe --

Serves _____ Preparation time _____

Difficulty Scale | 1 | 2 | 3 | 4 | 5 | Cooking time _____

Ingredients

Name   Weight/Measure/Amount

------------------------------------   ------------------------------------

------------------------------------   ------------------------------------

------------------------------------   ------------------------------------

------------------------------------   ------------------------------------

------------------------------------   ------------------------------------

------------------------------------   ------------------------------------

------------------------------------   ------------------------------------

Method

----

place recipes here

place recipes here

place recipes here

place recipes here

vegetable dishes

Recipe

Serves _____ Preparation time _____

Difficulty Scale | 1 | 2 | 3 | 4 | 5 | Cooking time   _____

Ingredients

Name   Weight/Measure/Amount

------------------------------------   ------------------------------------

------------------------------------   ------------------------------------

------------------------------------   ------------------------------------

------------------------------------   ------------------------------------

------------------------------------   ------------------------------------

------------------------------------   ------------------------------------

------------------------------------   ------------------------------------

Method

Recipe --

Serves _____ Preparation time _____

Difficulty Scale [1] [2] [3] [4] [5]   Cooking time _____

Ingredients

Name   Weight/Measure/Amount

-------------------------------- --------------------------------

-------------------------------- --------------------------------

-------------------------------- --------------------------------

-------------------------------- --------------------------------

-------------------------------- --------------------------------

-------------------------------- --------------------------------

-------------------------------- --------------------------------

Method

Recipe

Serves _____ Preparation time _____

Difficulty Scale [1][2][3][4][5] Cooking time _____

Ingredients

Name   Weight/Measure/Amount

----------------------------------   -----------------------------------

----------------------------------   -----------------------------------

----------------------------------   -----------------------------------

----------------------------------   -----------------------------------

----------------------------------   -----------------------------------

----------------------------------   -----------------------------------

----------------------------------   -----------------------------------

Method

Recipe

Serves _____ Preparation time _____

Difficulty Scale [1] [2] [3] [4] [5] Cooking time _____

Ingredients

Name   Weight/Measure/Amount

------------------------------- -------------------------------

------------------------------- -------------------------------

------------------------------- -------------------------------

------------------------------- -------------------------------

------------------------------- -------------------------------

------------------------------- -------------------------------

------------------------------- -------------------------------

Method

Recipe _____

Serves _____   Preparation time _____

Difficulty Scale   [1] [2] [3] [4] [5]   Cooking time _____

Ingredients

Name	Weight/Measure/Amount
-------------------------------	-------------------------------
-------------------------------	-------------------------------
-------------------------------	-------------------------------
-------------------------------	-------------------------------
-------------------------------	-------------------------------
-------------------------------	-------------------------------
-------------------------------	-------------------------------

Method

Recipe --

Serves _____ Preparation time _____

Difficulty Scale [1] [2] [3] [4] [5]   Cooking time _____

Ingredients

Name   Weight/Measure/Amount

------------------------------------   ------------------------------------
------------------------------------   ------------------------------------
------------------------------------   ------------------------------------
------------------------------------   ------------------------------------
------------------------------------   ------------------------------------
------------------------------------   ------------------------------------
------------------------------------   ------------------------------------

Method

Recipe --

Serves _____   Preparation time _____

Difficulty Scale | 1 | 2 | 3 | 4 | 5 | Cooking time _____

Ingredients

Name   Weight/Measure/Amount

-----------------------------------   -----------------------------------

-----------------------------------   -----------------------------------

-----------------------------------   -----------------------------------

-----------------------------------   -----------------------------------

-----------------------------------   -----------------------------------

-----------------------------------   -----------------------------------

-----------------------------------   -----------------------------------

Method

Recipe

Serves _____ Preparation time _____

Difficulty Scale [1 | 2 | 3 | 4 | 5] Cooking time _____

Ingredients

Name   Weight/Measure/Amount

-------------------------------   -------------------------------

-------------------------------   -------------------------------

-------------------------------   -------------------------------

-------------------------------   -------------------------------

-------------------------------   -------------------------------

-------------------------------   -------------------------------

-------------------------------   -------------------------------

Method

Recipe --

Serves _____   Preparation time _____

Difficulty Scale | 1 | 2 | 3 | 4 | 5 | Cooking time   _____

Ingredients

Name   Weight/Measure/Amount

--------------------------------   --------------------------------

--------------------------------   --------------------------------

--------------------------------   --------------------------------

--------------------------------   --------------------------------

--------------------------------   --------------------------------

--------------------------------   --------------------------------

--------------------------------   --------------------------------

Method

Recipe --

Serves _____ Preparation time _____

Difficulty Scale [1 | 2 | 3 | 4 | 5] Cooking time _____

Ingredients

Name   Weight/Measure/Amount

-----------------------------------   -----------------------------------

-----------------------------------   -----------------------------------

-----------------------------------   -----------------------------------

-----------------------------------   -----------------------------------

-----------------------------------   -----------------------------------

-----------------------------------   -----------------------------------

-----------------------------------   -----------------------------------

Method

Recipe

Serves _____ Preparation time _____

Difficulty Scale [1] [2] [3] [4] [5]   Cooking time _____

Ingredients

Name   Weight/Measure/Amount

-----------------------------------   -----------------------------------
-----------------------------------   -----------------------------------
-----------------------------------   -----------------------------------
-----------------------------------   -----------------------------------
-----------------------------------   -----------------------------------
-----------------------------------   -----------------------------------
-----------------------------------   -----------------------------------

Method

Recipe ---

Serves _____ Preparation time _____

Difficulty Scale [1 | 2 | 3 | 4 | 5] Cooking time _____

Ingredients

Name   Weight/Measure/Amount

-------------------------------------   -------------------------------------
-------------------------------------   -------------------------------------
-------------------------------------   -------------------------------------
-------------------------------------   -------------------------------------
-------------------------------------   -------------------------------------
-------------------------------------   -------------------------------------
-------------------------------------   -------------------------------------

Method

Recipe --

Serves _____ Preparation time _____

Difficulty Scale [1][2][3][4][5] Cooking time _____

Ingredients

Name   Weight/Measure/Amount

----------------------------------   ----------------------------------

----------------------------------   ----------------------------------

----------------------------------   ----------------------------------

----------------------------------   ----------------------------------

----------------------------------   ----------------------------------

----------------------------------   ----------------------------------

----------------------------------   ----------------------------------

Method

Recipe

Serves _____   Preparation time _____

Difficulty Scale   [1] [2] [3] [4] [5]   Cooking time _____

Ingredients

Name	Weight/Measure/Amount

Method

place recipes here

place recipes here

place recipes here

place recipes here

desserts

Recipe --

Serves _____   Preparation time _____

Difficulty Scale   [1] [2] [3] [4] [5]   Cooking time _____

Ingredients

Name   Weight/Measure/Amount

------------------------------   ------------------------------
------------------------------   ------------------------------
------------------------------   ------------------------------
------------------------------   ------------------------------
------------------------------   ------------------------------
------------------------------   ------------------------------
------------------------------   ------------------------------

Method

Recipe

Serves _____ Preparation time _____

Difficulty Scale | 1 | 2 | 3 | 4 | 5 | Cooking time _____

Ingredients

Name   Weight/Measure/Amount

---------------------------------   ---------------------------------

---------------------------------   ---------------------------------

---------------------------------   ---------------------------------

---------------------------------   ---------------------------------

---------------------------------   ---------------------------------

---------------------------------   ---------------------------------

---------------------------------   ---------------------------------

Method

Recipe --

Serves _____ Preparation time _____

Difficulty Scale | 1 | 2 | 3 | 4 | 5 | Cooking time _____

Ingredients

Name   Weight/Measure/Amount

------------------------------   ------------------------------

------------------------------   ------------------------------

------------------------------   ------------------------------

------------------------------   ------------------------------

------------------------------   ------------------------------

------------------------------   ------------------------------

------------------------------   ------------------------------

Method

Recipe

Serves _____ Preparation time _____

Difficulty Scale | 1 | 2 | 3 | 4 | 5 | Cooking time _____

Ingredients

Name	Weight/Measure/Amount

Method

Recipe --

Serves _____   Preparation time _____

Difficulty Scale | 1 | 2 | 3 | 4 | 5 | Cooking time _____

Ingredients

Name   Weight/Measure/Amount

------------------------------------   ------------------------------------

------------------------------------   ------------------------------------

------------------------------------   ------------------------------------

------------------------------------   ------------------------------------

------------------------------------   ------------------------------------

------------------------------------   ------------------------------------

------------------------------------   ------------------------------------

---

Method

Recipe

Serves _____ Preparation time _____

Difficulty Scale | 1 | 2 | 3 | 4 | 5 | Cooking time _____

Ingredients

Name   Weight/Measure/Amount

------------------------------------   ------------------------------------

------------------------------------   ------------------------------------

------------------------------------   ------------------------------------

------------------------------------   ------------------------------------

------------------------------------   ------------------------------------

------------------------------------   ------------------------------------

------------------------------------   ------------------------------------

Method

Recipe ---

Serves _____ Preparation time _____

Difficulty Scale [1] [2] [3] [4] [5] Cooking time _____

Ingredients

Name	Weight/Measure/Amount
----------------------------------	----------------------------------
----------------------------------	----------------------------------
----------------------------------	----------------------------------
----------------------------------	----------------------------------
----------------------------------	----------------------------------
----------------------------------	----------------------------------
----------------------------------	----------------------------------

Method

Recipe ....

Serves _____   Preparation time _____

Difficulty Scale | 1 | 2 | 3 | 4 | 5 | Cooking time _____

═══

Ingredients

Name   Weight/Measure/Amount

-----------------------------------   -----------------------------------

-----------------------------------   -----------------------------------

-----------------------------------   -----------------------------------

-----------------------------------   -----------------------------------

-----------------------------------   -----------------------------------

-----------------------------------   -----------------------------------

-----------------------------------   -----------------------------------

═══

Method

Recipe

Serves _____ Preparation time _____

Difficulty Scale [1] [2] [3] [4] [5]   Cooking time _____

Ingredients

Name	Weight/Measure/Amount

Method

Recipe ---

Serves _____ Preparation time _____

Difficulty Scale | 1 | 2 | 3 | 4 | 5 | Cooking time _____

Ingredients

Name	Weight/Measure/Amount
-------------------------------	-------------------------------
-------------------------------	-------------------------------
-------------------------------	-------------------------------
-------------------------------	-------------------------------
-------------------------------	-------------------------------
-------------------------------	-------------------------------
-------------------------------	-------------------------------

Method

Recipe ---

Serves _____   Preparation time _____

Difficulty Scale | 1 | 2 | 3 | 4 | 5 | Cooking time _____

Ingredients

Name   Weight/Measure/Amount

------------------------------------   ------------------------------------

------------------------------------   ------------------------------------

------------------------------------   ------------------------------------

------------------------------------   ------------------------------------

------------------------------------   ------------------------------------

------------------------------------   ------------------------------------

------------------------------------   ------------------------------------

Method

Recipe ....

Serves _____ Preparation time _____

Difficulty Scale | 1 | 2 | 3 | 4 | 5 | Cooking time _____

Ingredients

Name   Weight/Measure/Amount

--   --

--   --

--   --

--   --

--   --

--   --

--   --

Method

----

place recipes here

place recipes here

place recipes here

place recipes here

cakes, bakes and breads

Recipe _____

Serves _____ Preparation time _____

Difficulty Scale 1 2 3 4 5   Cooking time _____

Ingredients

Name	Weight/Measure/Amount
----------------------------	----------------------------
----------------------------	----------------------------
----------------------------	----------------------------
----------------------------	----------------------------
----------------------------	----------------------------
----------------------------	----------------------------
----------------------------	----------------------------

Method

Recipe

Serves _____ Preparation time _____

Difficulty Scale | 1 | 2 | 3 | 4 | 5 | Cooking time _____

Ingredients

Name   Weight/Measure/Amount

------------------------------   ------------------------------

------------------------------   ------------------------------

------------------------------   ------------------------------

------------------------------   ------------------------------

------------------------------   ------------------------------

------------------------------   ------------------------------

------------------------------   ------------------------------

Method

Recipe

Serves _____   Preparation time _____

Difficulty Scale [1][2][3][4][5]   Cooking time   _____

Ingredients

Name   Weight/Measure/Amount

------------------------------   ------------------------------

------------------------------   ------------------------------

------------------------------   ------------------------------

------------------------------   ------------------------------

------------------------------   ------------------------------

------------------------------   ------------------------------

------------------------------   ------------------------------

Method

Recipe

Serves _____ Preparation time _____

Difficulty Scale | 1 | 2 | 3 | 4 | 5 | Cooking time _____

Ingredients

Name   Weight/Measure/Amount

--------------------------------   --------------------------------

--------------------------------   --------------------------------

--------------------------------   --------------------------------

--------------------------------   --------------------------------

--------------------------------   --------------------------------

--------------------------------   --------------------------------

--------------------------------   --------------------------------

Method

Recipe

Serves _____ Preparation time _____

Difficulty Scale [1] [2] [3] [4] [5] Cooking time _____

Ingredients

Name   Weight/Measure/Amount

------------------------------   ------------------------------

------------------------------   ------------------------------

------------------------------   ------------------------------

------------------------------   ------------------------------

------------------------------   ------------------------------

------------------------------   ------------------------------

------------------------------   ------------------------------

Method

Recipe --

Serves _____ Preparation time _____

Difficulty Scale [1 | 2 | 3 | 4 | 5] Cooking time _____

Ingredients

Name   Weight/Measure/Amount

---------------------------------   ---------------------------------

---------------------------------   ---------------------------------

---------------------------------   ---------------------------------

---------------------------------   ---------------------------------

---------------------------------   ---------------------------------

---------------------------------   ---------------------------------

---------------------------------   ---------------------------------

Method

Recipe

Serves _____ Preparation time _____

Difficulty Scale | 1 | 2 | 3 | 4 | 5 | Cooking time _____

Ingredients

Name   Weight/Measure/Amount

--------------------   --------------------------------

--------------------   --------------------------------

--------------------   --------------------------------

--------------------   --------------------------------

--------------------   --------------------------------

--------------------   --------------------------------

--------------------   --------------------------------

Method

Recipe

Serves _____ Preparation time _____

Difficulty Scale | 1 | 2 | 3 | 4 | 5 | Cooking time _____

Ingredients

Name	Weight/Measure/Amount
----------------------------------	----------------------------------
----------------------------------	----------------------------------
----------------------------------	----------------------------------
----------------------------------	----------------------------------
----------------------------------	----------------------------------
----------------------------------	----------------------------------
----------------------------------	----------------------------------

Method

Recipe

_____

Serves _____ Preparation time _____

Difficulty Scale | 1 | 2 | 3 | 4 | 5 | Cooking time _____

Ingredients

Name   Weight/Measure/Amount

_____   _____

_____   _____

_____   _____

_____   _____

_____   _____

_____   _____

_____   _____

Method

_____

_____

_____

_____

_____

_____

_____

_____

_____

_____

_____

_____

_____

_____

_____

Recipe ....

Serves _____   Preparation time _____

Difficulty Scale | 1 | 2 | 3 | 4 | 5 | Cooking time _____

===

Ingredients

Name   Weight/Measure/Amount

------------------------------   ------------------------------

------------------------------   ------------------------------

------------------------------   ------------------------------

------------------------------   ------------------------------

------------------------------   ------------------------------

------------------------------   ------------------------------

------------------------------   ------------------------------

===

Method

Recipe _____

Serves _____ Preparation time _____

Difficulty Scale | 1 | 2 | 3 | 4 | 5 | Cooking time _____

Ingredients

Name   Weight/Measure/Amount

---------------------------------   ---------------------------------

---------------------------------   ---------------------------------

---------------------------------   ---------------------------------

---------------------------------   ---------------------------------

---------------------------------   ---------------------------------

---------------------------------   ---------------------------------

---------------------------------   ---------------------------------

Method

Recipe

Serves _____ Preparation time _____

Difficulty Scale | 1 | 2 | 3 | 4 | 5 | Cooking time _____

Ingredients

Name   Weight/Measure/Amount

-------------------------------------   -------------------------------------

-------------------------------------   -------------------------------------

-------------------------------------   -------------------------------------

-------------------------------------   -------------------------------------

-------------------------------------   -------------------------------------

-------------------------------------   -------------------------------------

-------------------------------------   -------------------------------------

Method

Recipe --

Serves _____ Preparation time _____

Difficulty Scale | 1 | 2 | 3 | 4 | 5 | Cooking time _____

Ingredients

Name   Weight/Measure/Amount

---------------------------------   ----------------------------------

---------------------------------   ----------------------------------

---------------------------------   ----------------------------------

---------------------------------   ----------------------------------

---------------------------------   ----------------------------------

---------------------------------   ----------------------------------

---------------------------------   ----------------------------------

Method

Recipe

Serves .... Preparation time ....

Difficulty Scale | 1 | 2 | 3 | 4 | 5 | Cooking time ....

Ingredients

Name   Weight/Measure/Amount

------------------------------------   ------------------------------------

------------------------------------   ------------------------------------

------------------------------------   ------------------------------------

------------------------------------   ------------------------------------

------------------------------------   ------------------------------------

------------------------------------   ------------------------------------

------------------------------------   ------------------------------------

Method

----

place recipes here

place recipes here

place recipes here

place recipes here

smoothies and juices

Recipe --

Serves _____   Preparation time _____

Difficulty Scale | 1 | 2 | 3 | 4 | 5 | Cooking time _____

Ingredients

Name   Weight/Measure/Amount

---------------------------------- ----------------------------------

---------------------------------- ----------------------------------

---------------------------------- ----------------------------------

---------------------------------- ----------------------------------

---------------------------------- ----------------------------------

---------------------------------- ----------------------------------

---------------------------------- ----------------------------------

Method

Recipe

Serves _____ Preparation time _____

Difficulty Scale   1 2 3 4 5   Cooking time _____

Ingredients

Name	Weight/Measure/Amount

Method

Recipe

_____

Serves _____   Preparation time _____

Difficulty Scale | 1 | 2 | 3 | 4 | 5 | Cooking time   _____

Ingredients

Name   Weight/Measure/Amount

-----------------------------------   -----------------------------------

-----------------------------------   -----------------------------------

-----------------------------------   -----------------------------------

-----------------------------------   -----------------------------------

-----------------------------------   -----------------------------------

-----------------------------------   -----------------------------------

-----------------------------------   -----------------------------------

Method

Recipe

_____

Serves _____ Preparation time _____

Difficulty Scale | 1 | 2 | 3 | 4 | 5 | Cooking time _____

Ingredients

Name   Weight/Measure/Amount

------------------------------   ------------------------------

------------------------------   ------------------------------

------------------------------   ------------------------------

------------------------------   ------------------------------

------------------------------   ------------------------------

------------------------------   ------------------------------

------------------------------   ------------------------------

Method

Recipe --

Serves _____ Preparation time _____

Difficulty Scale | 1 | 2 | 3 | 4 | 5 | Cooking time _____

Ingredients

Name	Weight/Measure/Amount
------------------------------	------------------------------
------------------------------	------------------------------
------------------------------	------------------------------
------------------------------	------------------------------
------------------------------	------------------------------
------------------------------	------------------------------
------------------------------	------------------------------

Method

Recipe

Serves _____ Preparation time _____

Difficulty Scale [1] [2] [3] [4] [5] Cooking time _____

Ingredients

Name   Weight/Measure/Amount

------------------------------------   ------------------------------------

------------------------------------   ------------------------------------

------------------------------------   ------------------------------------

------------------------------------   ------------------------------------

------------------------------------   ------------------------------------

------------------------------------   ------------------------------------

------------------------------------   ------------------------------------

Method

Recipe --

Serves _____ Preparation time _____

Difficulty Scale [1][2][3][4][5] Cooking time _____

Ingredients

Name   Weight/Measure/Amount

---------------------------------   ---------------------------------

---------------------------------   ---------------------------------

---------------------------------   ---------------------------------

---------------------------------   ---------------------------------

---------------------------------   ---------------------------------

---------------------------------   ---------------------------------

---------------------------------   ---------------------------------

Method

Recipe

Serves _____ Preparation time _____

Difficulty Scale 1 2 3 4 5   Cooking time _____

Ingredients

Name	Weight/Measure/Amount

Method

Recipe --

Serves _____ Preparation time _____

Difficulty Scale | 1 | 2 | 3 | 4 | 5 | Cooking time _____

Ingredients

Name   Weight/Measure/Amount

------------------------------   ------------------------------

------------------------------   ------------------------------

------------------------------   ------------------------------

------------------------------   ------------------------------

------------------------------   ------------------------------

------------------------------   ------------------------------

------------------------------   ------------------------------

Method

Recipe

Serves .... Preparation time ....

Difficulty Scale   1 | 2 | 3 | 4 | 5   Cooking time ....

Ingredients

Name	Weight/Measure/Amount

Method

place recipes here

place recipes here

place recipes here

place recipes here

special occasion menus

Starter --

Main Course --

Dessert --

Serves _____   Preparation time _____

Difficulty Scale | 1 | 2 | 3 | 4 | 5 | Cooking time   _____

Ingredients

Name   Weight/Measure/Amount

---------------------------------   ---------------------------------

---------------------------------   ---------------------------------

---------------------------------   ---------------------------------

---------------------------------   ---------------------------------

---------------------------------   ---------------------------------

---------------------------------   ---------------------------------

---------------------------------   ---------------------------------

---------------------------------   ---------------------------------

---------------------------------   ---------------------------------

---------------------------------   ---------------------------------

---------------------------------   ---------------------------------

---------------------------------   ---------------------------------

---------------------------------   ---------------------------------

Method

Starter ---

Main Course ---

Dessert ---

Serves _____ Preparation time _____

Difficulty Scale | 1 | 2 | 3 | 4 | 5 | Cooking time _____

Ingredients

Name   Weight/Measure/Amount

------------------------------   ------------------------------

------------------------------   ------------------------------

------------------------------   ------------------------------

------------------------------   ------------------------------

------------------------------   ------------------------------

------------------------------   ------------------------------

------------------------------   ------------------------------

------------------------------   ------------------------------

------------------------------   ------------------------------

------------------------------   ------------------------------

------------------------------   ------------------------------

------------------------------   ------------------------------

------------------------------   ------------------------------

Method

Starter --

Main Course --

Dessert --

Serves _____ Preparation time _____

Difficulty Scale [1 | 2 | 3 | 4 | 5] Cooking time _____

Ingredients

Name	Weight/Measure/Amount
------------------------------	------------------------------
------------------------------	------------------------------
------------------------------	------------------------------
------------------------------	------------------------------
------------------------------	------------------------------
------------------------------	------------------------------
------------------------------	------------------------------
------------------------------	------------------------------
------------------------------	------------------------------
------------------------------	------------------------------
------------------------------	------------------------------
------------------------------	------------------------------
------------------------------	------------------------------

Method